Slippery
SECRETS

by Desirée Moore

Published in the UK by
POWERFRESH Limited
Unit 3 Everdon Park
Heartlands Business Park
NN11 8YJ

Telephone   01327 871 777
Facsimile   01327 879 222
E Mail   info@powerfresh.co.uk

Copyright © 2006 Desirée Moore
Cover and interior layout by Powerfresh
Cover Design Sanjit Saha

ISBN 13: 9781904967613
ISBN 10: 1904967612

Printed in Malta by Gutenberg Press Ltd

Being a slim girl is all about attitude, not a number. Only 8% of women are naturally a size ten. For the other 92% you can still be a slim girl that is appropriate to the size you are meant to be. Stop trying to be something you are not.

Do you feel guilty every time you eat a chocolate biscuit so you then end up eating the entire packet? Slim girls don't feel guilty about eating chocolate biscuits so they don't over indulge.

Never eat anything at one sitting that you can't lift.

Miss Piggy

Do you go on weight loss diets but never keep the weight off when you start eating normally again? Slim girls don't diet because they know weight loss diets don't work. They just eat what they feel like, when they feel like it, in moderation.

Slim Girls Secret #1

Eat when you are hungry. Stop when you are full. Who said it had to be rocket science?

Do you believe you have to eat everything on your plate? Slim girls know that despite what some people say eating every morsel on your plate *won't* help starving children in the third world.

Do you think you have to a size ten to be beautiful? Slim girls know attractiveness is about attitude and they don't ascribe to skinny stereotypes of beauty. They just enjoy being who they are naturally.

Do you start each day by weighing yourself on the scales – and are you usually depressed by what the numbers say? Slim girls seldom weigh themselves and are never slaves to the numbers on a scale. They start the day feeling good about themselves.

Take a leaf from a slim girl and take a lifestyle approach to eating. Listen to your body and what it wants. Eat small and often. Eat broadly from all food groups. And most importantly, enjoy what you eat!

A diet is when you watch what you eat and wish you could eat what you watch.

Hermione Gingold

Do you drive yourself to despair worrying about how you look by comparing yourself to every skinny model you see in a woman's magazine? Slim girls don't compare because they don't care.

Do you turn to food when you are feeling emotional? Slim girls know that food can't solve your problems. Talk to a friend instead if you are feeling blue and view food as fuel for the body, not an emotional crutch.

Are you wearing old clothes that are one size too small? Slim girls always wear clothes that are comfortable, flattering and make them feel good.

Do you view food as the enemy? Slim girls view it as their friend – it provides them with energy to do all the things they want in their life and is also very delicious!

Slim Girls Secret #2

Be wary of any advert that includes emaciated models or models whose features are computer enhanced. Look at real people for role models of beauty.

Do you get your information about food, diets and health from magazines or TV shows? Smarten up – slim girls get their information from health professionals.

Are you one of the 59 percent of people who are currently on a diet even though you don't meet the criteria for being overweight? Slim girls say, 'Get a life!'

Do you count calories? Slim girls don't. They count their friends; count their blessings; count life's opportunities.

Do you constantly compare yourself to models in magazines and on the TV? Stop it right now! Slim girls notice real people's bodies and faces and love how diverse we are. 'Created' images have little power over them.

Part of the secret of a success in life is to eat what you like and let the food fight it out inside.

Mark Twain

Are you on a diet where you have to cut out a food group? Are you insane?! Slim girls know you need all the food groups to be healthy. Don't be sucked in by an unbalanced diet – someone out there is only trying to make money out of you.

Feeling blue about how much you weigh? Slim girls like themselves for who they are, not how much they weigh. Make a list of ten things you like about yourself that have nothing to do with how you look and read your list often.

Do you think being really skinny is healthy? Slim girls know that is merely fashionable, not healthy. Twenty years ago the average fashion model weighed 8 percent less than the average woman. Today she weighs 23 percent less. That's fashion.

Do you hate going to the gym and despair that it isn't helping you be slim? Slim girls find something they love and do that instead. It might be going to the gym, but is more likely to be dancing, swimming, horse-riding, making love...they enjoy moving their bodies for the sheer fun of it.

Slim Girls Secret #3

Fresh food is always the best food.

Do you think if you lose half a stone your life will be magically better? Slim girls know that:

a) no one else will probably notice you have lost weight and

b) your life won't be any different – you will still have the same old problems but you will just weigh less.

Do you often eat when you are not hungry? Slim girls wait until they feel like food. Eating food on an already full stomach is not satisfying.

Does your weight yo-yo up and down as you try one diet after another? Slim girls know there is no way you can be anything but what you are naturally and yo-yo dieting is the worst thing you can do for your health. Eat sensibly and be the size you were born to be.

Are you putting off going to the beach or taking up dancing until you lose some weight? Slim girls are out doing those things and having fun. Don't let your poor body image stop you from doing things in life.

Everything you see I owe to spaghetti.

Sophia Loren

Do you smoke cigarettes to keep thin? Slim girls know that you will probably put on weight if you quit, but you will be much healthier as a result. Go on, give up the ciggies today.

Do you think if you give up restricting your intake of food and instead eat normally that you will suddenly put on three stone? Slim girls trust their bodies and know that eating normally won't result in huge weight gain.

Slim Girls Manta

Start a revolution…stop hating your body.

Hey girl – are you naturally a size 16? Well you are in good company – 47 percent of the female population is naturally this size or more. Being slim is about attitude so be a slim sized 16 and enjoy your body.

Slim Girls Secret #4

Eat little and often. This is the key to successfully fuelling the body.

The dieting industry is a massive US$40 billion a year money-making venture. Slim girls don't contribute to this industry – they save their money for other, more enjoyable, things.

Are you scared of being fat? Slim girls aren't scared of fat – they are scared of nuclear war, terrorists, cancer or losing a loved one. Fat cells just doesn't rate.

Do you believe every image you see in the media is genuine? Slim girls don't. They know that many of the images are airbrushed, and touched up, or even several women pasted together to create the look that the advertiser wants. Slim girls surround themselves with real role models, not fake ones.

Do you think being a little overweight is bad for your health? Slim girls know that being a bit overweight is actually healthy if you exercise. Moderate exercise and nutritious food is the key to health!

In two decades I've lost a total of 789 pounds. I should be hanging from a charm bracelet.

Erma Bombeck

Are you envious of the very skinny looks of some models? Don't be. A high proportion of models suffer from anorexia nervosa. Slim girls realise how destructive eating disorders are and don't admire women who starve themselves (sometimes to death).

Do you try to ignore feeling hungry? Slim girls love feeling hungry because then they know it is time to eat – and food tastes so much better when you eat when your body wants to.

Have you just reached puberty and have suddenly put on some puppy fat? Don't worry about it! Slim girls know that you have to put on about some weight to become a woman and your body will settle down to its own naturally beautiful size. Don't diet to stop yourself growing up.

The waist is a terrible thing to mind.

Tom Wilson

Slim Girls Secret #5

Every time you see a magazine article telling you to be thinner or exercise more, ask, 'What are they selling?' instead of taking it as a personal accusation. Slim girls know a bit of cynicism is good.

Do you not eat all day but then binge all night? Slim girls know that skipping meals is likely to make you binge later because you are overly hungry. Eat small and often instead.

Do you think dieting is good? Slim girls don't. They know it is a risk factor for eating disorders, weight cycling and ironically, future weight gain. Studies show in two years time 99 percent of people on weight loss diets will have regained the weight, and often, even more!

Is the food you eat round but restricted? Think squares and triangles instead. Slim girls ascribe to good balanced square meals and use the traditional food pyramid as their base.

Do you surround yourself with negative people who are always putting you down? Slim girls surround themselves with positive people who make them feel good about how they look and who they are.

Gluttony is an emotional escape, a sign something is eating us.

Peter De Vries

Do you often eat on the run? Slim girls don't do this. They eat slowly and consciously. They like to eat in a calm environment, with others, where they can focus on the taste, smell and pleasure of good food.

Do you think dieting is good for children and teenagers? Slim girls know that dieting stunts the growth of young people – mentally, emotionally and physically. Instead of dieting teach young people moderate habits around food that will last them for a lifetime.

Are you always telling yourself you are fat and unattractive? Slim girls tell you to challenge your 'stinky' thinking as it is not correct. Girl, you are gorgeous!

Do you view most food as bad? Slim girls know that food has no moral value. They view all food as good, although some food they eat occasionally rather than everyday.

Slim Girls Secret #6

Never diet because diets rob you of energy and can cause you to feel fatigued and light-headed. Instead eat nutritious food so you can lead a full and active life and eat according to what your body needs.

Do you look a lot like your mother and feel resentful? Slim girls accept their genes. They can look at family photographs and recognise family characteristics without judging them.

Do you eat junk food everyday and wonder why you can't shed the pounds? Slim girls will treat themselves to junk food now and then and thoroughly enjoy the treat – but they will never eat junk food everyday.

On a fad diet and cutting out carbohydrates? Slim girls know that eventually you will binge on carbohydrate as your body needs carbs to function properly. Not only will you not lose weight in the long run, but you will also be unhealthier as a result.

Out of tune with your body? Slim girls know it is important to be aware of your appetite. Know what you feel like, eat when you are hungry and stop when you are full. Food should be a delicious energy-efficient fuel for your body!

Pessimist – someone who can look at the land of milk and honey and see only calories and cholesterol.

Quote Magazine

Do you eat your food too quickly and then feel too full? Slim girls eat slowly. They know the brain can take 20 minutes to register that you have had enough to eat.

Do you have a wardrobe full of clothes that you are saving for when you get 'thin'? Slim girls would never have outfits that don't fit. Donate them to a charity.

Do you think skipping breakfast is a way to lose weight? Don't start the day feeling sluggish – eat breakfast. Slim girls start the day energised.

Slim Girls Warning

Exposure to stereotypical images may be hazardous to your body image.

Slim Girls Secret #7

Appreciate all that your body can do: running, dancing, swimming, laughing, walking, loving…

Do you give yourself a hard time about the way you look? Slim girls give themselves lots of slack – no body's perfect.

Are you afraid of food? Slim girls love food. They find it nourishing, comforting, pleasurable and celebratory.

Have you put on weight after giving birth and can't shed the pounds as quickly as you would like? Slim girls don't stress about it. They know their body will settle down in its own time if they eat normally. They focus instead on enjoying their new baby.

Thinking about paying money to go on a diet? Slim girls know that quick weight loss schemes are among the most common consumer frauds and diet programmes have the highest customer dissatisfaction of any service industry. Needless to say, they spend their money in other ways.

One should eat to live, not live to eat.

Moliére

Do you ever guzzle huge quantities of soft drinks when you are thirsty and wonder why you aren't slim? Slim girls might have one soft drink now and then, but mostly they drink water.

Would you love to have a figure like a Barbie doll? Slim girls know that for the average women to look like Barbie she would need to grow nearly a foot in height, have a waist that measures 18 inches and add 4 inches to her bust-line. Oh...and then she wouldn't menstruate.

Are you on some crazy diet where you are eating bananas one day, apples the next and cucumbers the day after? Throw out the diet books and tune into your body. Eat what your body tells you it feels like and you won't go wrong.

Are you putting things on hold until you are your 'ideal' weight? A slim girl would never do that – life is much too short.

Slim Girls Secret #8

Eat slowly and savour every mouthful. Eat to enjoy your meal and also give yourself time to realise when you are full.

Do you think being thin will change your life? Slim girls focus on wellness, not thinness – they know that *wellness* will change their lives.

Are you one of the 79 percent of adolescents who have a negative body image? Work on your self-esteem. Slim girls know attitude is all important in life, not what you think are your perceived physical flaws. Chances are you will look back at photographs of your young self and see that beauty is, indeed, wasted on the young.